P9-CQQ-626

GOING UP WITH GROVER
A COUNTING BOOK

By Linda Hayward
Illustrated by Tom Leigh

A SESAME STREET/READER'S DIGEST KIDS BOOK

Published by Reader's Digest Young Families, Inc.,
in cooperation with Children's Television Workshop

Hello, everybody! I do not have time to stop and chat because I, Grover the elevator operator, am late for work.
One. . . . Going up!

2

10
9
8
7
6
5
4
3

1

Good morning, sir.
Two. . . . Going up!

Step right in, please.
Three. . . . Going up!

Watch the closing doors.
Four. . . . Going up!

10

9

8

7

6

4

3

2

1

5

Step lively, please.
Five. . . . Going up!

6

Move to the back.
Six. . . . Going up!

10
9
8
7

5
4
3
2
1

10

9

8

6

5

4

3

2

1

7

What a busy day.
Seven. . . . Going up!

Good morning to you, sir.
Come on, everybody! Make room!
Eight. . . . Going up!

10

9

7

6

5

4

3

2

1

8

Watch that wand, buddy.
Nine. . . . Going up!

Oh, my goodness!
Ten. . . . Going up!

9
8
7
6
5
4
3
2
1

10

Swimming pool!
Everybody off!
PHEW! Time for my break.

Closing time.
Going down!

Ten. . . . Going down!
Hey, watch it!

Nine. . . . Going down!
Excuse me, sir, but you are
dripping on my foot.

10

8

7

6

5

4

3

2

1

9

Eight. . . . Going down!
Have a nice evening.

Seven. . . . Going down!
Maybe I should have been
a bus driver, instead.

10
9
8
6
5
4
3
2
1

7

Six. . . . Going down!
I thought that marching
band music would never stop.

5

Five. . . . Going down!
Nice hat, miss.

10

9

8

7

6

4

3

2

1

Four. . . . Going down!
This has been a very
long day.

Three. . . . Going down!
Watch the closing . . . doors, sir.

Two. . . . Going down!
Oh, my!

One. . . . Going up!